A Red Wagon Year

Written by **Kathi Appelt**

Illustrated by

Laura McGee Kvasnosky

It's a table for the winter birds

F e b R

A Valentine Express

A prairie schooner in disguise

A red-eared turtle's nest

A cart for blossoms, pink and blue

A rolling masterpiece

A fancy float with bows and stars

A bathtub for the beast

A schoolbus for our school supplies

A ship from far away

A tractor for the harvest . . .